AHMAD AND THE LOST CHILDREN

Written by
Sajjedah
Dewji

Ordering Information:
Quantity sales. Special discounts are available on quantity purchases by corporations, associations, and others. For details, contact the distributor at the address below.

 A catalogue record for this book is available from the National Library of Australia

Lantern Publications
info@lanternpublications.com
www.lanternkids.com.au

"Lantern Kids" is a subsidiary of Lantern Publications

ISBN- 978-1-922583-22-2

First Edition

Illustrations: Leyla Teymoorinejhad | **Design:** Naser Hasani |
Editor: Dr Abidali Mohamedali

This book is dedicated to the children of Palestine, who are being robbed daily of their right to live a normal life.

Some references have been made to specific recurring incidents. However, any resemblance of the characters to anyone living or deceased is purely coincidental. We advise readers to keep abreast of the continuing atrocities on the children of Palestine (and all the oppressed Muslims) and, at the very least, pray for their patience and ultimate victory.

BiSMiLLAH

Ahmad is not too far away

an African grey with a beautiful red tail

"Allah the Almighty created me just like you", he says,

"He can come and visit us every single day

My little children... tell me... do you pray

Remember, Allah the Almighty is with you

He is not at all far away

5

I'm going to tell you a little story today
About a little girl called Laila and a boy named Layth
So come on then, let's go.
Let's go to a land not so far away. To a land called Palestine,
and see how our little brother and sister are feeling today.

So close your eyes and fly to a land not so far away.
And remember, this journey is a story about today.
Where there were once big buildings, a football
ground, a swing and a slide to play.
Where a lot of little children used to pray and stay.

8

"Look under that mountain," says Ahmad
"Is that a mountain or a broken home?

10

Is this where little kids stay?
Let's look for Layth and Laila.
They are waiting for us. They know we are
visiting them today

"There they are", says Ahmad
"I found them!
Little Layth and Laila, are you okay?"
With a little nod, Layla and Layth smile and say,
"Alhamdulilah... God the Almighty is with us to stay."

12

Layth and Laila are only yet still small,
Did they not know that life would have turned
upside down, just after the month of Ramadhan
when the minarets in al-Aqsa lit tall?

Ahmad sits on Lailas' shoulder and
screams, "watch your step, Layth!" he
says, "Please don't fall."
I know there was a building where
you stand which was very tall!
"How is it that our playground is
gone Ahmad?" asks Laila,
"What about our Mama or Baba and
our baby Hamza?
Do we still have to be so strong?"

14

15

16

"Hold my hand, Laila, and look up at the sky," says Ahmad.
"It's dark but yet so beautiful. Is that a shooting star or the moon, or is God, the Almighty, watching down on us? We are fond of Him and His Prophet and the Ahl ul Bayt; may peace be upon them."

"Why did I not get to go to school?" Layth asks Ahmad. "I wanted to get on a bus just like everyone."

18

Write on my paper the letters of the alphabet.

Play with my friends and learn from my beautiful teachers!

Can I also have a packed lunch that I can take?

And a scientist, an artist, a lawyer, a doctor or a teacher I can become?

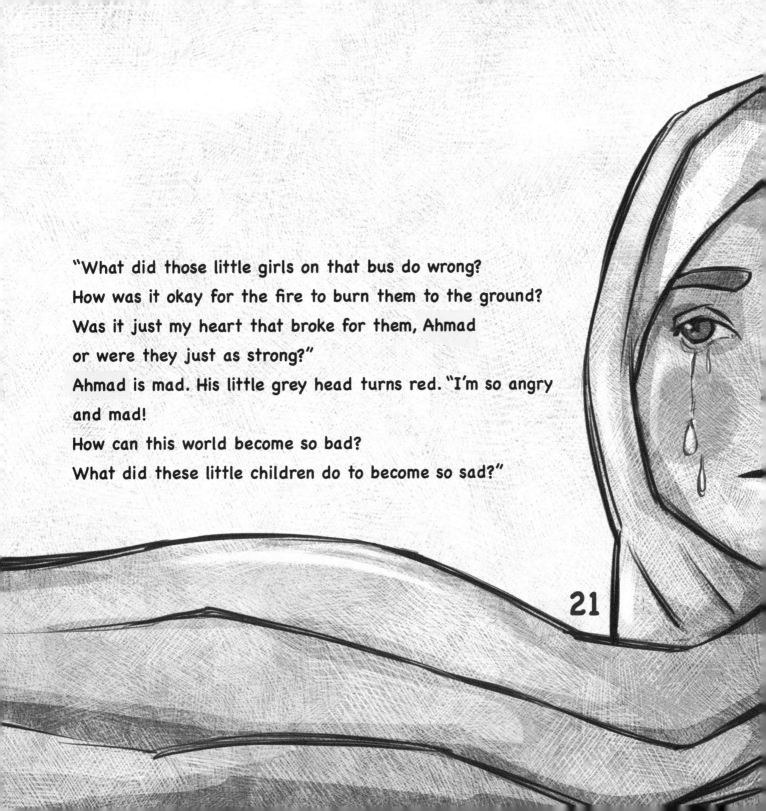

"What did those little girls on that bus do wrong?
How was it okay for the fire to burn them to the ground?
Was it just my heart that broke for them, Ahmad
or were they just as strong?"
Ahmad is mad. His little grey head turns red. "I'm so angry
and mad!
How can this world become so bad?
What did these little children do to become so sad?"

21

"I want to play with cars and run on sandy beaches too!" Layth says to Ahmad.

"Will we ever feel the ocean under our toes? Build a sandcastle to jump and play with and feel the soft breeze on our faces?

Will I hear you run after me and hide while you giggle, Laila?"

22

"I want to learn to drive too. Just like
Baba", whispered Layth
"and go out for a drive, lick some ice cream
too, fill up fuel in the gas station...
What about having some chicken wings? Or a
run around the park, Ahmad?
All these dreams we have, they have stolen!"

24

"Hold me tight tonight", whispers Ahmad. "As we look up at the sky, remember Allah the Almighty sees everyone that's wrong and right." "The sky is filled with smoke and darkness", says Layth, "but there is a twinkle of a star not too far away. The moon that will follow us until dawn."

27

28

"But then I'm scared", says Laila.

"I'll hug you tight when you hear anything," says Ahmad.

"Don't think of the blasts, bombs and drums. Just be strong."

29

"What if I cry?" whispers Laila. "We have
no home, no roof, no water. The wolves
watch us like they are going to eat us.
What about our little goldfish? Did he also
do something wrong?"

30

31

"God is here with us," says Layth.
Ahmad smiles. "Indeed He is! He's not too far away.
Stand tall and be strong.
Because above the bombs and the blasts Allah, the Greatest, is louder and stronger than that!"

33

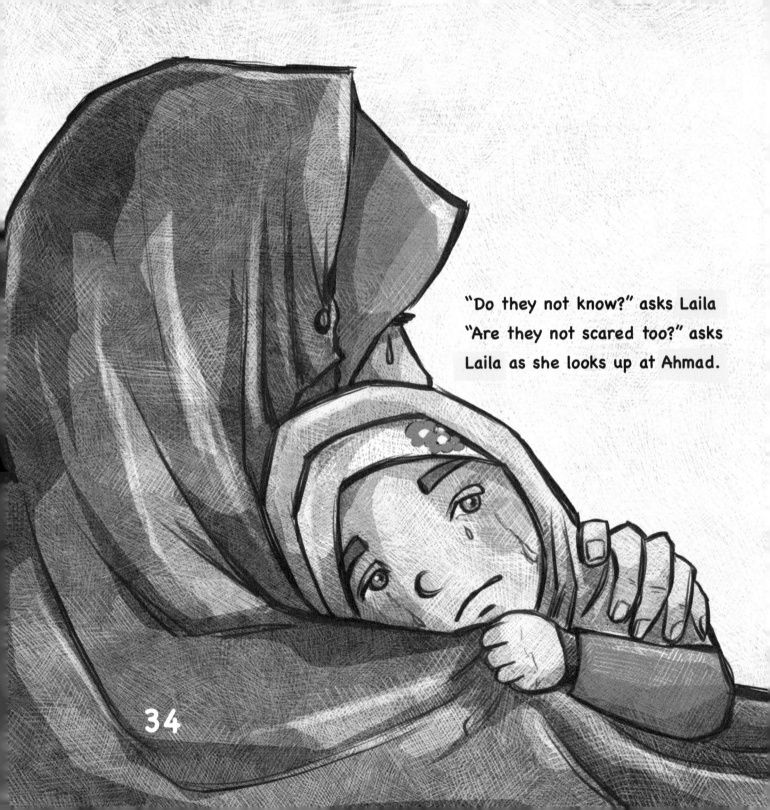

"Do they not know?" asks Laila
"Are they not scared too?" asks
Laila as she looks up at Ahmad.

34

"For every heart that believes will stay strong," says Ahmad.
"There is no one who can take your faith. For God is with us, and He will certainly correspond."

"Do you think He was watching Baba cry while trying to save us, Layth?

Where is our home? Mama was scared too. She held me tight as the dust filled my eyes."

"Don't be scared, little one", says Ahmad.

"Because you always have to remember from Allah, we came and to Allah, we belong."

36

"There is a special place for little children in heaven,
they say. Have you seen it? Have you been there,
Ahmad?" says Laila.
"Oh yes, Laila", says Ahmad. "You will play in streams
and long valleys and big mountains" "We will have a
Mama and a Baba and toys that we have never seen
before and this is only because we are patient and with
Allah, the Almighty,
the Holy Prophet and the Ahl ul Bayt, we have a bond."

38

"I'm happy now", says Layth. "Because I know, Ahmad, that God is listening! Do they also know that their actions are poisoning
and they will also face a day of questioning?

40

Are they not afraid of that day?
Where their books will be dark
and grey?

41

Ahmad flaps his beautiful wings, "Allah is most merciful, they say,
He is listening to everything today.
And for each deed with a punishment and reward everyone will pay!"
"I feel the hand of Allah, the Merciful, on my head", says Layth.
"Think about it... He is with us, and so are all the people that have prayed!
So, close your eyes tonight", says Ahmad, "and think of Allah,
the All Watching. You know He is always listening.
Can you hear His mercy? It is surely
awakening!"

43

"So, there you go, Laila. God is always listening", says Ahmad. "Just close your eyes and remember Him, for this little, small prayer will be the start of a new awakening."

"See you soon again, Ahmad. Thank you for visiting us today, for you make us smile whenever we think of you.

And we can't wait to see you again one day.

Don't worry. You have taught us to be healthy and strong.

We are never alone. The twelfth saviour is soon going to come. He will appear with justice and truth, and with him we will belong!"

9 781922 583222